Heroes to
Colour

PaRragon

Bath • New York • Cologne • Melbourne • Delhi
Hong Kong • Shenzhen • Singapore

This edition published by Parragon Books Ltd in 2018

Parragon Books Ltd
Chartist House
15–17 Trim Street
Bath BA1 1HA, UK
www.parragon.com

ISBN 978-1-4748-9153-0

Printed in China

Peter Quill was born on Earth, but always drawn to the stars. He became the intergalactic adventurer, Star-Lord, and now leads a fearless team known as the Guardians of the Galaxy.

Gamora was trained to be an unparalleled warrior by the
Super Villain, Thanos. But after rebelling against him,
she now seeks forgiveness for her past crimes.

Genetically-modified Rocket is a mechanical and engineering
genius, who can make incredible things from scrap.

Groot is the last surviving member of a tree-like alien race.
He is a creature of immense strength but few words.

Drax the Destroyer is fuelled by revenge but, as part of the
Guardians of the Galaxy, he must learn to put the needs
of the universe before his own.

The *Milano* is a one-of-a-kind vehicle for a one-of-a-kind team. It can easily outrun anyone who tries to chase the Guardians.

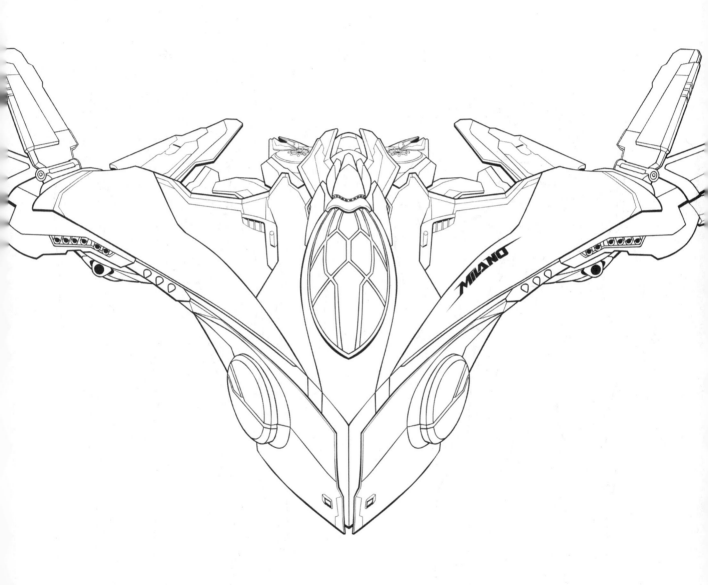

Together, they are the Guardians of the Galaxy.

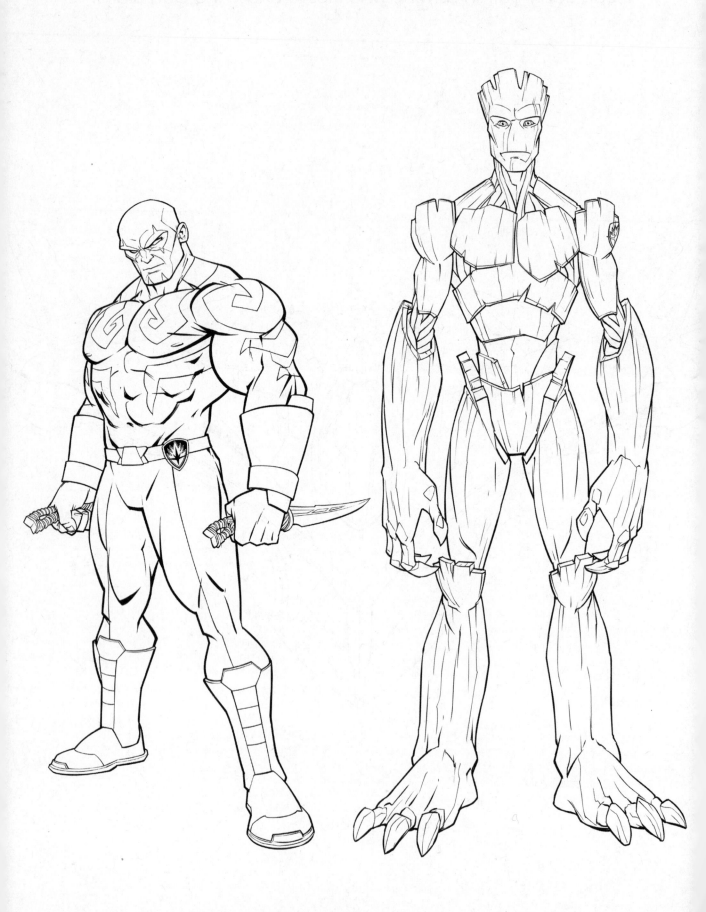

Ready to protect the universe from anyone who attacks it.

Rocket and Groot used to work together
as small-time intergalactic thieves.

Gamora was once known as the 'most dangerous woman in the galaxy'. Now she puts her skills to good use protecting the universe and saving lives.

Star-Lord is equipped with a special helmet
that helps him survive in space.

After Groot sacrificed himself to save his team members,
Rocket took a branch of him and planted it in a pot,
allowing Groot to regrow. The hero lives!

Drax takes everything very literally.
So be careful what you say around him!

Groot can send out bright spores which provide light,
even in the darkest depths of space.

Rocket makes sure the Guardians always
have the best technology and gadgets.

Star-Lord and Gamora work together to defeat
every new threat they come across.

Although Groot only says "I am Groot", the Guardians always know what their little friend means.

Peter Quill's trusty starship, the *Milano*, has an impressive range of interstellar weapons, and can easily overpower even the most intimidating enemies.

The Guardians of the Galaxy are always ready
to defend, using a little good, a little bad
or a little bit of both!

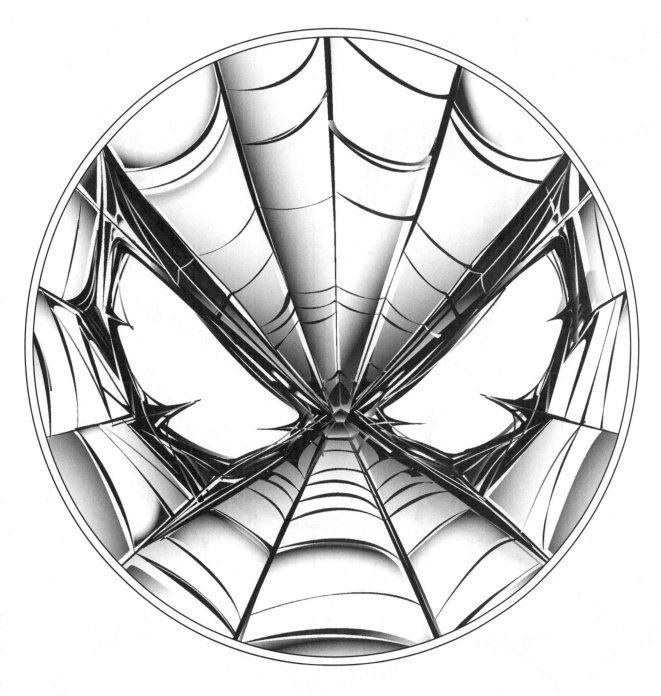

"Uh-oh, my spidey-sense is tingling –
there's danger in New York City."

Vulture has flown in to cause havoc! His mechanical harness gives him superhuman strength and the ability to fly.

Vulture circles high over the city,
looking for his next target.

The Amazing Spider-Man swings into action to defeat him!

In an alternative universe, a twist of fate meant that Midtown High student Gwen Stacy was bitten by a radioactive spider instead of Peter Parker – turning her into Spider-Gwen!

At first Spider-Gwen used her new talents for personal gain and attention, but she soon learned that with great power comes great responsibility.

Dr Octopus was once a well-respected scientist.
Then a terrible lab accident fused his greatest creation,
a harness with four mechanical tentacles, to his body.

Villain-for-hire Rhino is equipped with nearly indestructible armour, superhuman strength and horns which can puncture solid metal.

Spider-Man's symbiote suit seemed like the greatest crime-fighting tool. It gave him enhanced spider-strength and an unlimited source of webbing, but it also had a dark secret.

The suit was a living thing that wanted to take over Spider-Man's body! He managed to get rid of the suit, but it would later return as one of his deadliest foes – Venom!

Anya Corazon gained incredible spider-like powers after a freak incident. Now she uses them to help protect New York City, as Spider-Girl!

Whether Spider-Man is scaling a skyscraper
or swinging from rooftops, this wall-crawling
hero is always ready to save the day.

When Peter Parker first became Spider-Man, he didn't have time to make a fancy suit. So he made do with his functional, but maybe not so fashionable, proto-suit.

Green Goblin loves to cause chaos with his explosive pumpkin bombs and razor-sharp batwing projectiles.

After an experiment with reptile DNA went wrong,
Dr Curt Connors was transformed into a monstrous
creature known as Lizard.

In an alternative world, the corrupt Alchemax corporation has taken over New York City. Miguel O'Hara is inspired by tales of the legendary Spider-Man and becomes a new-age hero.

Miles Morales became Kid Arachnid in an alternative world, after Peter Parker gave his life to protect New York City.

Spider-Girl watches over the city, on the look out for any threats.

With great power, comes great responsibility.

Watch out villains! Kid Arachnid can discharge
a powerful electrical Venom Strike capable
of paralyzing with one touch.

Spider-Man fires his web-shooters and swings to the rescue!

When he's not protecting Earth, Iron Man is genius billionaire businessman, Tony Stark.

Steve Rogers became Captain America
when he was given the Super-Soldier Serum
during World War Two.

You wouldn't like to meet Bruce Banner
when he's angry – he turns into the Hulk!

A chance encounter with Captain America
brought out the inner hero in Sam Wilson,
and he became Falcon.

Before she worked for S.H.I.E.L.D., Natasha Romanoff –
also known as Black Widow – was a Russian spy.

Clint Barton trained as an acrobat in the circus.
He uses these skills as Hawkeye!

Thor is from another world, known as Asgard.
He is honourable, mighty and worthy of the power
of Mjolnir, his enchanted hammer.

Black Panther was granted superhuman powers after eating a mystical heart-shaped herb.

Vision was originally created by the evil robot Ultron to help destroy the Avengers. Instead, he rebelled against his creator and joined them to fight against the villain.

War Machine wears a modified version of the Iron Man suit created by his best friend, Tony Stark.

As the astonishing Ant-Man, Scott Lang handles the jobs 'too small' for other Super Heroes.

Wasp has the amazing ability to shrink in size and fly.
She can also discharge powerful electric shocks
called 'wasp stings' from her hands.

You and the Avengers must work together
to save the world from disaster.

After he was exposed to a faulty version of the
Super-Soldier Serum, Johann Schmidt became Red Skull.
He is the leader of Hydra, a group of terrorist soldiers.

Anton Vanko created the Whiplash suit
so he could battle against Iron Man.

Loki is the God of Mischief.
He is determined to destroy Earth.

"Loki has hacked into S.H.I.E.L.D.'s defence systems and stolen a top-secret weapon," Nick Fury tells the Avengers. "We have to get it back."

Director Fury sends Thor to find his stepbrother, Loki.

Loki believes that he is the rightful king
of his and Thor's home world, Asgard.

"Looks like we're keeping this in the family,"
says Thor when he finds Loki.

CRASH! The brothers begin to battle.

"Nothing like a bit of sibling rivalry," sneers Loki.
But the God of Mischief knows he is beaten.

Loki may have lost this round,
but Thor knows his brother will return.

S.H.I.E.L.D. is alerted to a threat in New York City.
Nick Fury sends Captain America to check it out.

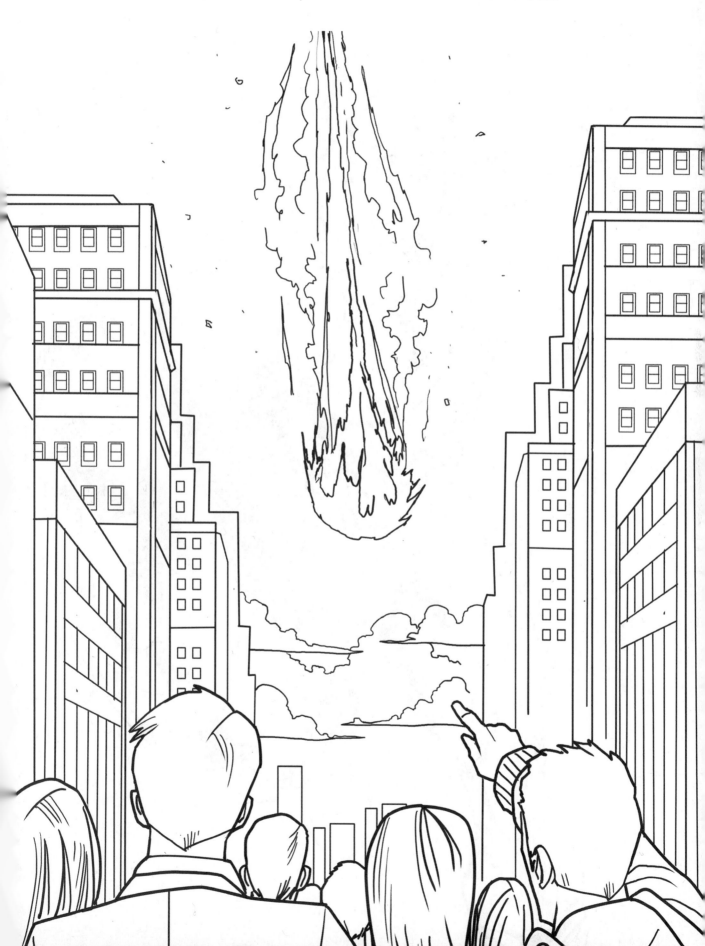

Captain America sees the smoke from downtown New York and races towards it.

Cap's oldest enemy, Red Skull, is waiting for him!

"Need a hand ... or a wing?" asks Falcon,
as he soars down to join Cap.

Two Avengers are better than one.

"Not today, Red Skull!" shout the Super Heroes.

Red Skull is defeated! He is no match
for Falcon and Captain America.

Ant-Man and Wasp work together to prove
heroism comes in even the smallest sizes.

The newest Avengers are assembled
and ready to help defend the Earth.

As long as there are villains ...

... there will be Super Heroes to protect us.

And those Super Heroes are called ...

the Avengers!